In the beginning

darkness was everywhere.
God said,
"Let there be light!"
And so light shone into the darkness.

Now there was day and night.

God created the air and the sky—

an enormous sky, with fluffy clouds.

He made the wide oceans and the deep seas.
He made rolling waves and splashing spray.

God made dry land—
the high hills and the tall mountain

6

the deep valleys and the wide plains.
God saw it, and he was pleased
with the land he had created.

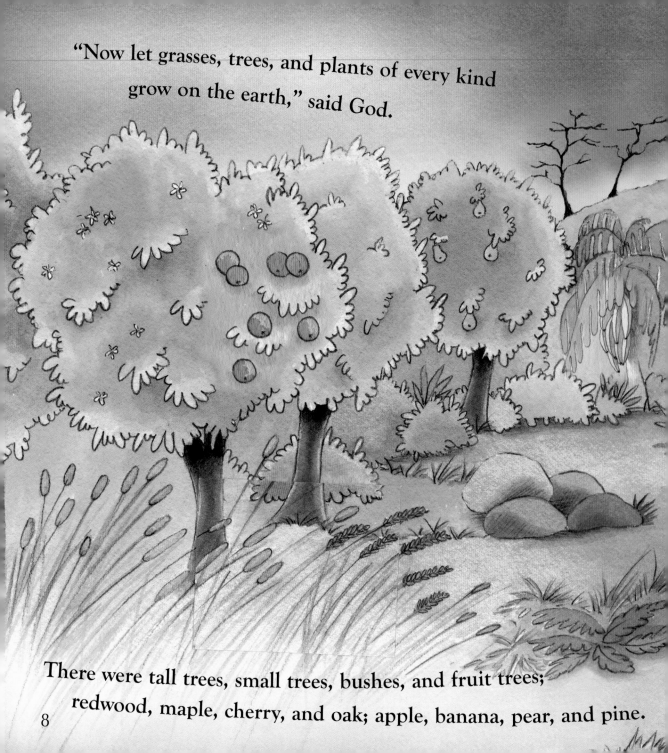

"Now let grasses, trees, and plants of every kind grow on the earth," said God.

There were tall trees, small trees, bushes, and fruit trees;
redwood, maple, cherry, and oak; apple, banana, pear, and pine.

8

There were climbing plants
and prickly plants,
and waving grasses,
ripe with corn.

There were flowers everywhere.
Red, yellow, orange, purple, pink, and blue,
they scented the air.

10

lies, lavender, daisies, roses, and honeysuckle.
God was pleased with all the growing things he had created.

11

God filled the sky with magnificent things—
the hot, blazing sun for daytime,
and the silvery moon at night.

He gave the comets fiery tails.

He made millions of twinkling stars
to shine in the darkness of space.

13

"Let there be living things in the water," said God.
So he made schools of fish
to swim in his vast oceans:

big fish, little fish, round fish, flat fish—
so many flapping tails and
waving fins!

14

He made teeny-tiny sea-creatures
and great big sea-monsters.
And God was pleased
with the swimming things
he had created.

15

"Let there be living things in the air," said God. So he filled the air with millions of birds and insects.

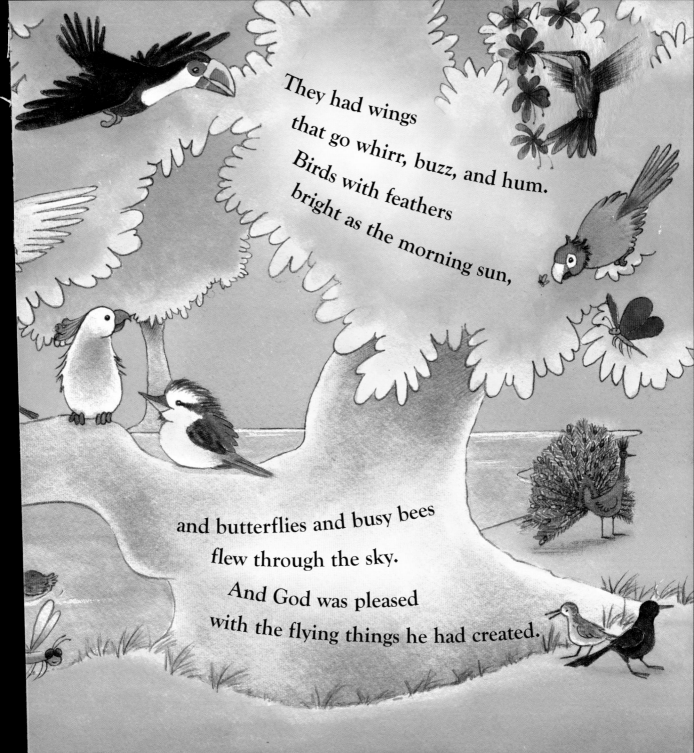

They had wings
that go whirr, buzz, and hum.
Birds with feathers
bright as the morning sun,

and butterflies and busy bees
flew through the sky.
And God was pleased
with the flying things he had created.

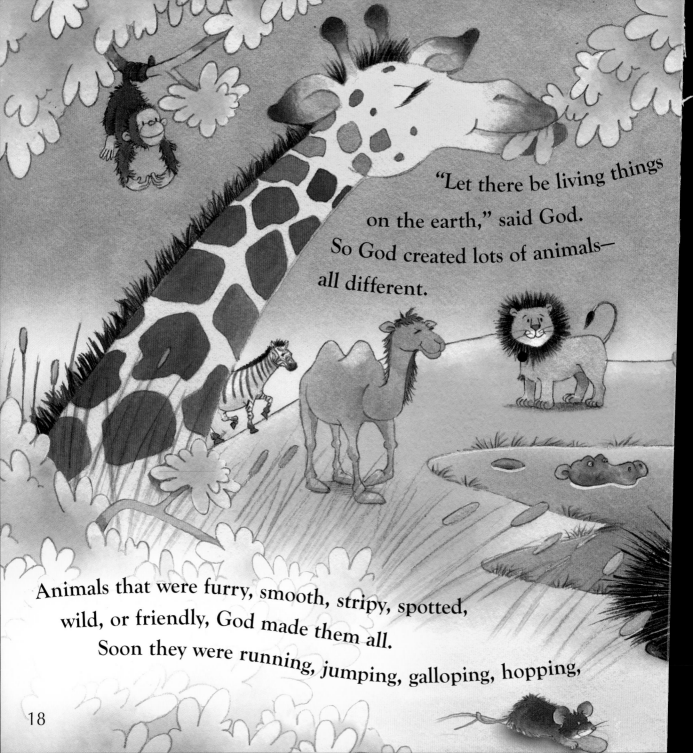

"Let there be living things on the earth," said God.
So God created lots of animals—all different.

Animals that were furry, smooth, stripy, spotted, wild, or friendly, God made them all.
Soon they were running, jumping, galloping, hopping,

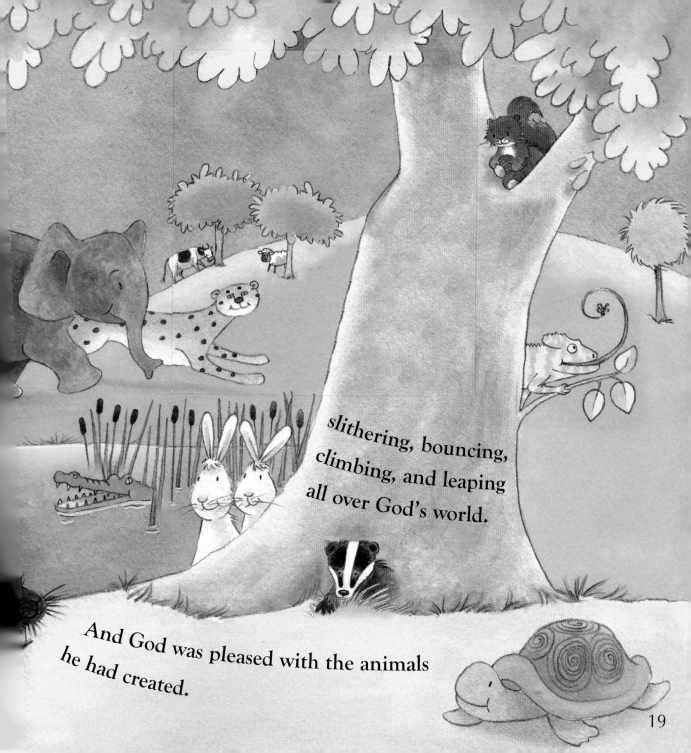

slithering, bouncing, climbing, and leaping all over God's world.

And God was pleased with the animals he had created.

19

Last of all, God created people.

"Let there be people!" said God.
And God made the first man
and called him Adam;
and he made the first woman
and called her Eve.

He made them to be his friends,
and he asked them to take care of this world.

God was very, very pleased with everything he had created.

God loved the world he had created

and he loved everything in it

And after that, God rested.